OLD MAC DONALD
Had a Farm
PICTURES BY MORITZ KENNEL

gb GOLDEN PRESS
Western Publishing Company, Inc.
Racine, Wisconsin

Ninth Printing, 1976

Old Mac Donald had a farm,
Ee-igh, ee-igh, oh!

And on that farm he had some chicks,
Ee-igh, ee-igh, oh!

With a chick chick here
And a chick chick there,
Here a chick, there a chick,
Everywhere a chick chick . . .

Old Mac Donald had a farm,
Ee-igh, ee-igh, oh!
And on that farm he had some ducks,
Ee-igh, ee-igh, oh!

With a quack quack here
And a quack quack there,
Here a quack, there a quack,
Everywhere a quack quack . . .

And on that farm he had some turkeys,
Ee-igh, ee-igh, oh!

With a gobble gobble here
And a gobble gobble there . . .

And on that farm he had some pigs . . .

With an oink oink here

oink oink there . . .

And on that farm he had some cows . . .
With a moo moo here
And a moo moo there

And an o

And on that farm he had some donkeys . . .

With a hee haw here
And a hee haw there . . .

And on that farm he had some sheep . . .

With a baa baa here
And a baa baa there . . .

Here a baa, there a baa,
Everywhere a baa baa.
With a hee haw here
And a hee haw there,

Here a hee, there a haw,
Everywhere a hee haw.
With a moo moo here
And a moo moo there,

Here a moo, there a moo,
Everywhere a moo moo.
With an oink oink here,
And an oink oink there,

Here an oink, there an oink,
Everywhere an oink oink.
With a gobble gobble here,
And a gobble gobble there . . .

Here a gobble, there a gobble,
Everywhere a gobble gobble.
With a quack quack here,
And a quack quack there . . .

Here a quack, there a quack,
Everywhere a quack quack.
With a chick chick here,
And a chick chick there . . .

Here a chick, there a chick,
Everywhere a chick chick.
Old Mac Donald had a farm,
Ee-igh, ee-igh, oh!